Colin Dennis

Mars 1 -Earth 0

Illustrated by
Ira Baykovska

Published by Sprocket and Tubs

For Lottie and Matthew

HMS Disorder

There is a boat that's half afloat.
Its sails are torn and tattered.
It has no guns, there's only buns,
And the Captain likes his battered!

Having sailed around the Seven Seas,
The crew, they cause a rumpus.
The Captain sailed away, you see,
With a rusty, broken compass.

And when a Pirate ship sails by,
The crew they're all a' shudder.
For it's hard to steer, that is quite clear,
With a mermaid sat on the rudder.

The Bosun now gets jittery,
Because the Captain's under scrutiny.
He'd better get it right next time, or else,
There's going to be a mutiny!

High up in the Crow's Nest,
The lookout's spotted land.
A swaying palm with coconuts,
And angry crabs upon the sand!

'Abandon ship!' the Captain cries.
Alas, he's lost his mind.
But, set adrift, with a short-sharp-shrift.
The Captain tows the line!

Kitchen Troll

Some Trolls do live among us.
Some Trolls do hide away.
Some Trolls are mean and boastful,
But some just want to play.

There is a Troll who has a gift,
He is something quite unique.
For in his kitchen he has learned,
It's fun to take a leek!

His knife is sharp. His talent rare.
His skill, it knows no bounds.
And since he's changed his culinary ways,
He's shifted twenty pounds.

Amid the chaos and the noise,
Of his Trollish family.
He stews and chops, and he concocts,
A fearsome recipe.

But not many Trolls have got the guts,
To do away with carrion.
To break the rules. Be no one's fool.
And become a vegetarian!

Mars 1 – Earth 0

Ready for take-off, ready to blast,
Engines firing, freedom at last.
Up through the clouds, into the night.
Retro's burning, spaceship in flight.

Behind us now, blue planet small.
We'll see you again, no time at all.
Flashing bright, the buttons squeak.
Here comes Mars, let's take a peek.

One small step, one giant bound.
Say 'hello' to new friends we've found.
A game you say. A mighty roar!
We've brought a ball. Hey! Maybe we'll score?

Losing with grace, winning is nice.
It's your day, you've thrashed us twice.
'Beginners luck!' that's what we say.
But well-done Mars; we've seen fair play.

So sad to say, return we must.
It's been such fun, kicking dust.
But should you ever stray our way.
Come visit Earth, come play away!

Cosmic Ray

Cosmic Ray is on his way,
To planets far and wide.
He's off to explore the galaxy,
With his puppy by his side.

The wonders of the universe,
Are marvellous to see.
He's even brought his watering can,
To plant his favourite tree.

With fuel enough for one big trip,
And honey from his bee.
He'll easily get to Jupiter,
Then it's back in time for tea!

Puddlesplash Lane

Jumping in the puddles, dancing in the rain.
Now's the time we run amok, in Puddlesplash Lane.

Thunder clouds clapping, gushing water fills the drain.
All our senses heightened, in Puddlesplash Lane.

Wellies full of water, squelchy socks, and toes in pain.
We have to keep on running, in Puddlesplash Lane.

Minds are free of muddles, with friends so full of cuddles.
Together chasing rainbows, in Puddlesplash Lane.

Forever to be grateful, it's here that we remain.
Dancing in the puddles, of Puddlesplash Lane.

The House on Morning Star Hill

On Morning Star Hill, there sits a house,
It's as big as a castle, but quiet as a mouse.
And I will tell before you ask,
About this house and its magical task.

You see, when night creeps in and darkness falls,
A rain of arrows shoots up from the walls.
To pierce that curtain of inkwell stain,
And remind the clouds to let it rain.

But, of all the arrows that fly into the night,
Few chosen ones can bring in the light.
For each of those shafts is given a charge,
To wake the stars both bright and large.

When, come the morning bright and early,
You leave your sleep, all warm and curly.
Go walk that hill, or miss your chance,
To see morning stars, their magic dance.

So, put on your boots, your hat, and your coat,
Wrap a woolly scarf around your throat.
Then cheerfully chase that morning chill,
Collecting your arrows, on Morning Star Hill.

Sea Anemone

Sea anemone, her hair all aglow.
See the anemone, moving so slow.

Sea anemone, she follows the flow.
See the anemone, see where she goes.

Sea anemone, now diving below.
See the anemone, her treasures in tow.

Iona Moon

Iona Moon called down to me.
'Search the stars to set yourself free.'

'Me?' I sighed, 'how can this be?
I am but small. The size of a pea.'

She took my hand. She held me tight.
Then up we flew towards the night.

Past the stars that twinkled bright.
Iona Moon, she felt so right.

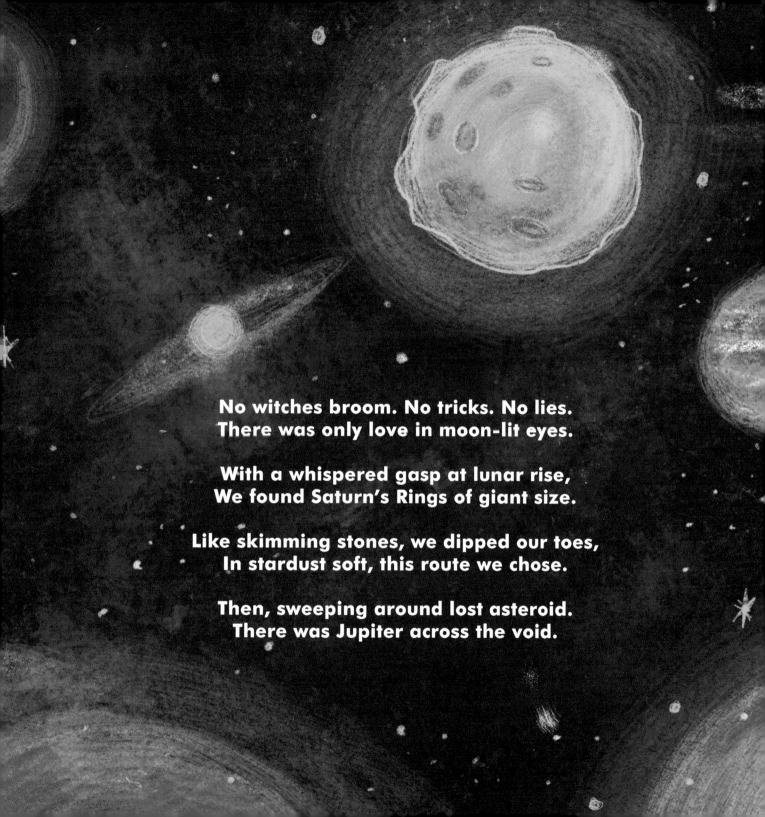

No witches broom. No tricks. No lies.
There was only love in moon-lit eyes.

With a whispered gasp at lunar rise,
We found Saturn's Rings of giant size.

Like skimming stones, we dipped our toes,
In stardust soft, this route we chose.

Then, sweeping around lost asteroid.
There was Jupiter across the void.

But while on this cosmic tide of joy,
I was still her little boy.

And as the sun was heading west,
My guiding star, she would not rest.

Until in my bed and fast asleep.
I own the Moon. Now mine to keep.

Printed in Poland
by Amazon Fulfillment
Poland Sp. z o.o., Wrocław